Ben Gets

story by Jenny Alexander
illustrated by Ken Stott

Ben wanted to go into the bathroom

but Tessa was in the bath.

"Hurry up!" shouted Ben.

"Go away!" shouted Tessa.

Ben was angry.

He went to Tessa's bedroom.

He took Tessa's dress

and hid it under his bed.

"Where is my dress?" said Tessa.
Mum said, "It's there somewhere."

"Your bedroom is a mess.
Tidy it up," said Mum.

Bump went Tessa's books.
Thump went Tessa's boots.

Slam went her door.

Ben was pleased.
He went off to play.

He forgot that he was angry.

He forgot that Tessa's dress was under his bed.

At teatime, Mum said, "Did you find
your dress?"
"No," said Tessa.

"I hid it," said Ben. "I was angry.
You took so long in the bath."

"It was horrible to hide my dress," said Tessa.

"But he **has** given it back,"
said Mum.

Tessa looked at Ben.

"You made me tidy my room,"
she said, "and that made me get dirty…

so now I will have to go in the bath
again!"